MW00773387

The Me in Me

D Kay

DORRANCE
PUBLISHING CO
EST. 1920
PITTSBURGH, PENNSYLVANIA 15238

Dorrance Publishing Co
585 Alpha Drive
Pittsburgh, PA 15238
Visit our website at www.dorrancebookstore.com

ISBN: 978-1-6376-4303-7
eISBN: 978-1-6376-4617-5

Introduction

This world we are in is a big place; it is quite simply very easy to get lost in it. There are so many places: industrial thriving cities, vast flourishing jungles, deep and wide valleys, intertwined trees amidst winding forests, mysterious and deep interconnected oceans. There are so many diverse people coming from so many backgrounds with so many different ideas and perspectives with lives, abilities, and stories of their own. But, with these places, things, people, and visions, where do we fit in? See, I know that books will tell you that this world we are conscious in is the only planet that sustains life, the only place of true existence. But, what if I tell you that I know of other worlds just as vast and complex as the one we are in now, and I know of them for certain because I have been to them; they are very much real and alive, being able to sustain life with an infinite number of outcomes and circumstances, and I am not too vain to admit that out of all the worlds I've been to there are so many more that I have not.

Yet, I sense your disbelief. So, I will tell you a little about one. This world doesn't exist quite in the term of existence as you might think, but it is quite real. You can never go to this world, but I might see you there, although it might not be you as you see yourself. No, you have a world like this world too; it's a great place with so many blissful things that can bring tears of joy. Yet, all the same, these worlds can be awful places as well with unspeakable darkness, unbearable pains, and unexpected tragedies. These worlds that are filled with frightening disappointments and unremorseful joys hold many similarities to our current world. Exploring it can occupy a lot of your time, if not all of it. But, try not to get stuck there because you are in this world now, and this is where you need to be. But, when all is quiet, you can sneak off into your other world; and, in that world, you can find out who you truly are in all worlds.

Yet, onto the world at hand that I am speaking about now. In this world, there is a man or boy. I'm not sure of his age, and I suspect he doesn't have one yet, but I suppose it doesn't matter. Age is not real. We limit things because of age, like it makes some sort of difference how old you are. See, you are either alive or dead, here or gone. Now is the perfect time to do what you believe you should do. What I do know is that this boy in some ways is in all of us, whether a rich or poor boy or girl, peasant or king, whether deemed as an angel or devil, whether considered worthy or unworthy in any or all circumstances; because, in some ways, just like this boy, we have these characteristics in one way or another. We are all considered either good or bad to someone somewhere. Either we are great, worthy, and cherished people to someone somewhere or we are awful, unworthy, and despised people. Yet, no need to worry, just be who you are, be the way you want to be, and let them worry about how great or awful you are.

For this boy though, what I want you to know is what I am almost certain this boy has forgotten; it's something we can forget as well, that we are special and needed integral pieces to this world. We are what makes this world. Without one of you this world is not what it is now because through some divine intervention you are alive at this moment, and you have something that you are meant to contribute to make this world complete. You must never forget that every one of us is here now, and we are what makes this moment relevant. Never see yourself as too great or too insignificant. You are unique and so must see yourself as you really are because that is the greatest accomplishment.

To clear up confusion, let me tell you how I concluded what I assumed this boy has forgotten and what I want you to remember. This boy lives on a small island in the vast ocean. It is a beautiful island being kissed by a golden sun with many rainforests and gardens bearing lots of vegetation and fruit, ripe in colors and minerals; there are many exotic animals that create a marvelous ecosystem that is envied by all other surrounding islands. The days seem to be blissful with a warm, soothing, bright sun that is followed by cold, crisp, refreshing winds at night that cool the body and free minds of their daily concerns, a slender cut of heaven for most, but to this boy it isn't that so much. I'm not telling you he doesn't enjoy being there; he just isn't sure where he belongs, concerned that he is missing out on something great that the island couldn't offer. I know it seems that he has most everything a boy could want, and the island is as close to perfection as most worlds would care to offer, but sometimes even if you are in the sun all the time the snow can seem like a piece of heaven that is kept secret by angels that forget to tell you because they are astonished by its breathtaking beauty.

That is what happens to the boy. He wants something different; he is fascinated by the things that he hasn't yet seen. He wants more; he wants to contribute to the world. The guide that is in this boy's heart urges him that he is coming to a point in his life where he doesn't just need to take from life, he needs to start to give back to it. The feeling that he is given by the island and the great and marvelous lessons are no longer enough. They are now unpleasing and unsettling. He needs more, and that is exactly what his eminent heart and mind are telling him. He doesn't just need to occupy space; he needs to make the space he occupies better. He is called, just like all of us are, to make a more thriving and suitable world for when we leave it. When we leave this world, it shall be better than when we were put in it, for it is our world now and in our care. We are the ones who can choose how much more thriving and suitable it will become.

He often thinks of this and ponders how he could make this world better. His question is often answered with a depressing, clueless conclusion of, "I am unsure." He thinks, "I want to be remembered by everyone; maybe I will become a great, strong warrior, fighting in pivotal world changing battles, slaying the world's most fearsome enemies and becoming a beloved hero and protector of all."

But, reality becomes apparent that he is not the strongest warrior. He doesn't know how to fight, and to not be the best on the battlefield will lead to a sure death. So, he quickly changes his idea and takes another approach. "I want everyone who respects my opinions to come to me with their burning questions, and I will give them undoubtable wisdom, so I will become a great scholar and teacher and share my opinions and wisdom to all so that they will become wise and create a more knowledgeable world." But, this boy couldn't think of any wise opinions to share, and without internal knowledge how can you bestow wisdom?

The boy, stuck in his endless decisions, sighs in a hopeless rage and looks down at his reflection in the ripple-filled, moving ocean offshore and says, "I have nothing, no great talent, nothing unique. I don't belong here. I don't belong there. I can't just do anything for if I do I will be unhappy just as I am now doing nothing, but I know I've got to do something. Yet, I have no clue what that something may be. What will make this mundane life worthwhile? What will make moving beneficial? When will my reality be half as good as my dreams and desires?"

In a frantic rage, he rushes to his home and goes directly to his mother screaming, "I don't belong here or there. I just don't belong, but I need to go somewhere." He races out the door as his mother quickly shouts to him trying to plead and reason with him, but he is gone into the night. In a panic, the boy runs wildly through the island's beach unsure of where he is going. He is just running to get away from his uncertainties. Then, just offshore the boy sees a sailboat at the dock. He jumps onto it screaming, "I will sail until I can't sail no more!"

The Storm

Emotion is a great motivator; however, it is a terrible guide. All worked up by his anxious thoughts and an overwhelming fear of mediocrity, he jumps onto the sailboat and sails right into a crushing storm at sea. The waves are crashing, giving off roars of thunder as they clash and collide into one another. The otherwise quiet water is in a violent rage as it shook and threw the boy in his tiny sailing ship completely off course. This boy now has another problem other than just finding out what he is to be or where he should go. He is lost not only in his head but now also in reality. The fear for his life gives him overwhelming thoughts which disguised the original problem that got him in the middle of the storm to begin with. Then, just as quickly as these storms came, they left. The storm of his emotions and the storm at sea simultaneously subside. The boy could see clearly now even though he was lost; and, as the darkness of night and the fear of survival entered his mind, he says in a meek and humble whisper, "Oh, how I wish I knew how to get home." The boy just sits there hunched over with his hands cupping his head and knees touching his elbows, floating along the ocean much like a seed floats away from a tree, the one thing that made it strong, that brought it life, and sustained its life. The boy is the seed completely isolated from his comfort and everything he knows. He is away from the one place he knows, the place that knows him.

Thinking of what he has done and how he has let his emotions get the best of him, he sits helplessly in sorrow. He is now in a worse situation than the one he originally created and has nobody to blame but himself. He gave way to the winds and waves letting them take control over his direction, though it cannot be assumed he knew where he was going before. The boy floated into the black, unpredictable night and the night just seems to get darker and less clear. The boy becomes afraid because the darkness surrounding him leads to uncertainty. The pitch blackness envelopes his being making him unsure of what is ahead of him or what is behind him, above or below him. The gloom and murkiness make it impossible to know if he is moving closer toward home or if he is drifting farther away. It is uncertain what he is running from in the first place. Yet, now more than ever, he is positive of his misgivings, apprehensive about the future while hesitant about the past.

The Lighthouse

In an abrupt change of thought the boy decides to look up and sees a glimmer of light in the distance. Such a brilliant choice the boy makes stumbling out of the cloud of darkness and into the light, leaving the paralyzing fear behind him as he embraces the warm light ahead. It's easy to get stuck in a hole from time to time when focusing on one's defeats, problems, or circumstances. Feeling helpless, one looks down and cries out into the darkness, "I am stuck!" Only after facing the problem at hand and deciding to look up can one realize how to get out of the hole and resolve any difficulties. Looking up, one can slowly start to climb out of the darkness. After all, if the goal is a brighter future, one must keep looking up; focus on the brightness ahead and follow one's dreams. Whether the decision is forced upon him or chosen, the boy looks up to see the light in the distance. The light gives him hope to press on, a hope that encourages his hand to grab the rope to set his sails, and he sails straight for the light burning in the darkness. While sailing close to the light he realizes that the radiant glow is coming from what looks to be somewhere in the middle of the sky, just standing there all alone. The light to him is symbolic of his innate goodness. His conscience perceives this feeling and compels him to further inspect the glowing orb. He realizes it's not just floating but is attached to something, something is holding it up. He discovers it is a lighthouse.

3

Where there is a lighthouse there must be ground around it, so he decides to land there and rest until the break of day. Then, he will try and make it back home when it becomes much brighter. As the boy arrives at the lighthouse he realizes how dark it is between there and the shore and a crippling fear comes over him. But, he still has a spark of hope from seeing the light and finding somewhere to land, so as he begins to walk, "If I can just keep my eyes on the light, I can get there and get out of all this darkness." With his head up and eyes forward, he begins to walk toward the light, walking confidently as he feels like now he has the courage and hope to make it out of this darkness and find his way back to his little island of safety, oblivious to the dismal darkness that exists outside of his vibrant home.

Yet, as the darkness makes itself apparent and envelopes him, uncertainty creeps its pessimistic roots into his brain. Fear settles in and he feels his confidence fade in the night just as a fleeting thought passes and the awareness of the dark rushes back into his mind. He hears the evil cracks and chatters of the night and in a soft, crackling, eerie voice he hears a, "Whoooo are you?" Feeling the chills that begin to trickle down his spine after hearing the voice, the boy speeds up his steps. The ground beneath his feet thud with each aggressive stride. The voice comes back in a much louder, more demanding, and clearer tone, "Whoooooo are you?"

In a full-on terror, the boy takes off into a dead sprint, jumping past stones and pushing away limbs of trees heading straight for the lighthouse. He feels the presence gaining on him and looks back for a split-second causing him to slip to his knees. With no hesitation, he jumps back up and runs faster than he has ever run before. Right as he feels this thing at his back, he reaches the lighthouse door and slings it open quickly slamming the door behind him. With a sigh of relief and a feeling of fatigue, he puts one hand on the stair rail and slowly drags his feet up the spiral staircase to the light at the top of the lantern room. The long climb to the top of the tower leads to a glassed-in, multi-sided room from which a lens stands on a pedestal projecting its beam across the vast ocean. From this dank and musty room can be seen the deck outside around the top, also known as the gallery. But, Malachi is hesitant to step outside now, rather preferring the glass enclosure.

The Owl

After arriving at the top of the lighthouse, he looks out onto the ocean in hopes that he might be able to see a glimpse of his home that he lost, but the light shows nothing but water for miles upon miles into the distance. Discouraged, he begins to slump down when out of the corner of his eye he sees that one of the lighthouse's windows is missing. As he turns in a panic to find something to block the hole with, he sees two sharp, raptor-like claws come in through the open window. The boy yells in a terrified, helpless voice, "Please, show me mercy!" The creature replies with a soft, concerned voice, "I don't mean to startle you, but Whooooo are you?" The boy looks up to see a rather large, old-looking owl. The boy says to the owl sadly, "I am lost and afraid." Quizzically, the owl hoots, "Hooow did you become lost?"

Shamefully, the boy replies, "I was looking for something when a storm blew me off course. Then, it was dark and scary, and now I am more lost than I was before." The owl says, "I see; I presume you are afraid of the dark." Sure of himself, the boy replies with a sharp and loud voice, "Of course I am, aren't you?" The owl laughs in a dismissing crackle, "I am not! I love the night, after all I am an owl." Realizing his stupidity, the boy replies, "Of course you are not afraid; you're an owl. But, for me, I just wish for morning whenever it gets dark." The owl says calmly, "The day and the night are not so different. They are in a lot of ways one and the same. They can both bring joy, yet they can still both bring fear. They can teach you a lot. Both together make a day, not one or the other; you need them both, and I feel like both night and day can help you find what you have lost." The boy quickly asks, "How can night and day help me?" The owl coos, "Think of this, things do not get from bad to good or good to bad in a snap, just like you did not get lost in a second. There are many things that got you lost, and it will take a string of things to get you found. That is exactly like night and day; it gradually goes from light to dark and from dark to light. Things just won't change in an instant. But, if you look close enough, you can see the day changing even in the darkest of times just like I can see you getting closer to finding your way back home. That is why we should be happy even when it's dark or when we're lost because we know that light will come in time. But, if we see darkness as a miserable time and wish for it to be over, then we'll spend our days dreading the night and our nights wishing for the day to return, and we won't be happy in either situation. You never know when or where you will find something you lost, so don't be afraid of the darkness because sometimes it's the only time we can see our own light. It shines brighter at night illuminating the truth within, glowing from the darkness, just like you found this little lighthouse from so far away in what appears to be the darkest night." The boy calmly replies, "I guess I just need to see the best in things." The owl gives him a joyful look of approval, "Get some rest for you have a great journey ahead, and I must enjoy the night." As the old owl begins to fly away the boy shouts, "Wait! Do you know where my home is; will I ever find what I'm looking for?" The owl, while taking off into flight replies, "I don't know my friend, all I know is if you do not believe that you will, then you will never find it; rest assured, you will know what to do in time." As the owl flies off, the boy with a concerning plea yells out, "But, how?" Then, he hears a distant echo from the owl, "You'll feel it!"

The boy, with his back to the lighthouse wall, slowly slides down into a sitting position and lets out a dissatisfied, exhausted sigh. Disheartened and afraid, he walks to the broken window and thinks to himself, "Is this all life is, just random existence?" Just then, his sight is captivated by a large, hanging, full moon. He thinks to himself, "I have probably gone 347 days without going outside and looking at the moon, I mean truly being in the present moment and gazing upon its radiant light. It is so much older than anyone alive today, but when I see it, I mean truly look at it, the light seems so new, unblemished like it may never die in a life of everything fading away and getting sick. It seems as if the moon could shine forever, and it may. I just look at it, and it is riveting. It makes you feel without saying a thing that there is a purpose to all of this. There is a reason I am alive; the moon quietly reveals so much that it quite literally lights up the entire world. It makes me believe there must be a heaven because I can almost see a free sincere place that cannot be described by words. It could be eternal, but it doesn't have to be. But, I think it's like the moon, free and pure and giving off light, not defined by words, thoughts, shapes, space, or time, just alive in an existence under a unity of many individuals." The boy's thoughts ramble on as he falls asleep under the stars.

As the night turns to day, the boy is awakened by a beaming light that enters the lighthouse window. The boy yawns and groggily says, "Morning already?" The boy stands, stretches, and looks out the lighthouse window gazing upon the wide, blue ocean thinking to himself how beautiful it is as radiant sun glimmers off the ocean's waves looking like thousands of scattered diamonds. The boy says to himself, "How beautiful the sea is here, but I long to get home." As he circles around the lighthouse staring off into the distance in hopes that he can see his comforting safe-haven that he calls home, his eyes land upon what he thinks could be a mountain. A jolt of energy rushes through his body as his sense of hope is reclaimed. Seeing that piece of land, the boy makes his way down the lighthouse steps to his sailboat and begins to set sail for the land that he found. The boy takes in the beautiful setting as he feels a sense of courageous pride for discovering the mountain that could hopefully help him find his way home.

The Dog

Arriving closer to what he thought was a mountain, he realizes it isn't a mountain at all. Instead, it is a giant, sturdy, man-made wall. The boy, intimidated by the wall's powerful structure, thinks, "This wall was built by someone; there must be a civilization inside of it. I hope they are kind, and maybe they can tell me how to get home." Still, hopeful but with apprehension setting in, the boy speaks, "I wonder what they are keeping from getting in that wall or maybe what are they holding within it?"

After landing his small sailboat on his newfound hope that was this island, the boy is taken aback by the size of this giant mountain wall that looks like even the ground-breaking underneath it could not waver or even crack the foundation. Trembling in fear the boy thinks maybe he should look around and find another place. Just as he turns around he hears a pattering of footsteps coming to a scraping halt as he feels his legs get swept out from under him flipping him through the air before gravity plummets him to the ground with his face to the sky; and, sighing with a tooth grinding pain he feels four paws land on his torso and a wet, long, slimy streak across his face. The boy, with a disgusted look on his face, peers up to see huge, psychotic, excited eyes staring him directly in the face.

Before the boy can even get a word out, he is startled by a rapidly enthusiastic, "Sorry, I am just so excited to see a new friend! Let's play, gotta catch me!" In milliseconds, the dog takes off running and barking out excitedly. The boy thought to himself, "Although a little off color and a tad insane, he seems nice enough."

Pushing his cares aside, the boy joyfully takes off after the dog running through the forest, laughing and smiling as he eagerly chases his new friend. The boy has a moment of relief from his problems and worries and simply enjoys himself, running so fast that the air felt like wind at his back, like he could almost spread his arms out and bring his feet off the ground and fly through the green, vibrant forest. The boy continues to chase after his new friend until the dog makes an abrupt stop next to the proud, giant, city wall. The boy is astonished by the walls giant metal plating which looks like gods and devils coating the structure to keep any mortal creature from scratching its surface. The boy mumbles out in fear asking the dog, "Wwwhat is this?" With a joyful, energetic response the dog barks, "Awall!"

Malachi Meets the Funny Man

L ooking up at this massive fortress, the boy feels a small tap on his shoulder. He looks down to see a small, round man with brightly colored clothes and bright yellow-orangish hair.

Keeping to himself he thinks, "What a funny looking man," but of course the boy says nothing aloud. The funny looking man with his hand behind his back standing straight up in a rather confident stance says, "Hi! Hello, what is your name? You give me your name, and I'll do the same." The boy says, "Hello, my name is Malachi, and yours?" The funny man replies, "I am Sir Charles Elmer. I'm glad to say, and why are you outside the gate on a day like today?" Discouraged, the boy sighs, "I had become frustrated, so I left my home to sail the sea for a while. Then, a storm came and lunged me off course. I tried to find my home, so I sailed here to find someone who could get me back on track to my little island that I long for so dearly." The funny little man says, "I see. I don't know where home is, but come and follow me." So, the boy whistles for the dog who seems to be staring at the sky, captivated by it like it was his first time seeing it. Yet, it was clearly not. Malachi whistles again for the simple dog which breaks the spell the sky has over him. The dog lets the boy know he's coming, barking and wagging his tail the whole way. Happily reaching the boy, the dog jumps up to greet him with a wet lick across his face.

Following the funny man to the corner of the wall the boy asks, "What is inside that gate?" The funny man stops dead in his tracks and turns around, standing as tall as the short man could, with his chin sky high in the air as if it would make him appear taller. He replies in a rather matter-of-fact kind of way, "Oh, my boy, it's my home city you see. But, I am outside of its gate because it was taken from me." Then, quickly the funny man jerks around and says, "Come along, right this way, stop your talking cause you can't stop the day." The boy continues to follow the funny man even though he is a little put off by his demeanor.

Malachi Meets the Stragglyman

They come to a corner near the city gate, and behind this corner sits a very tall, straggly looking man with old, raggedy clothes that have rips and moth-eaten holes all in them, and there is a hat covering his face suggesting he is sleeping. He looks like he is old, exhausted, and in need of sleep. But, the sun is being rude, shining down on him continuously and reminding him it is morning and the day still needs to move along. Quite purposefully the funny man lightly pokes the straggly man, and the old man yawns very loudly as he removes his hat from his face and puts it on his head. He says, "What can I do for you my friends?" The funny man replies, "This is Malachi. He is lost you see. I hope you can tell him where he might should be." The old man says, "I see; where are you trying to go, my young friend?" The boy begins his tale, "I am from an island that is somewhere in the ocean, and I just wanna go back home." The old man replies, "Hmmm, I don't know where that is, but I am from northeast of here. I can tell you how to get from here to there and everywhere in between, but I have never been to an island. Yet, I believe I can help you since your home is across the ocean. Let's go to the ocean and see what we can find." The jittery dog woofs in anticipation of the outing, "Yes! I love the ocean, and on our way we can run and play and explore." The old man looks down with a smile of approval and says, "Yes, of course we can." The funny man chimes in, "Let's run and search and search some more, cause when you're lost it's best to explore."

The infectious excitement of his new friends makes Malachi feel relieved and full of joy as they all start walking toward the ocean. The rather observant old man points across the way, "Look my friend, I can see the ocean over the hills." The boy looks through the never-ending forest past beautiful green, rolling hills onto a great, wide, blue ocean. And, a smile intrudes upon the boy's sadness as he once again has the hope that he can make it home. The dog, seeing the boy's sheer joy says, "Come on, I'll race you to the shore." The dog takes off into the forest as the boy chases behind him dodging trees as they head for the forest exit.

The Dragon

Right as they were going past the last tree line, the boy smacks straight into a big, black object. Upon impact, Malachi feels scales like an armored tank and heat from burning coal against his face. As he plummets to the ground, he hears words from the beast's mouth speaking in a proper yet sinister tone, "Why are you here peasant?" The boy pleads to the beast in a terrified voice, "I'm just trying to get home. I came to your land by mistake." Leaning over and looking into the boy's fearful eyes, the dragon asks, "Where are you from?" Cowering beneath the disgusting creature too afraid to run, Malachi begins to tremble like a leaf in the wind. The boy answers timidly, "I am from a little island across the ocean." As he stretches his neck into an upright position, the dragon spews his fiery breath as he answers, "Oh, yes, you must be speaking of the one with plenty of vegetation and animals." Jumping up and down with great excitement, Malachi exclaims, "Yes, that is precisely the place. Can you tell me how to get there?" Pondering the boy's question, the dragon taps his long, scaly claw upon his sharp front teeth seemingly replaying something in his mind, "Hhhmmm..." Suddenly, the boy notices a small, red light beginning to form in the pit of the all-black beast. It starts to shoot up the serpent's throat. Startled with fear, the boy puts his hand on the dog's head; and, just as the flames meet the giant black dragon's cheek, the old straggly man jumps out with the funny, chubby man on his back and grabs both the boy and dog as an engulfing ball of flame burns the ground where they were just standing. Racing through the forest with the quickness of a rabbit, the old straggly man yells for them to hang on. The vile beast in frustration roars an earthquake starting bellow and blows a blanket of fire across the forest. Engulfed in a sea of fire, the entire forest is burned to ashes. With the speed of a cheetah, the straggly man jumps over the giant gap in the earth and runs himself and his friends to safety. The dragon roars, "I will take you home, boy, and you will watch as I destroy your precious island." Then, the dragon spreads his giant black wings, that momentarily black out the sun and turn the whole land dark, and flies over the giant city walls.

In the Cave, Plotting the Dragon's Demise

Diving into a cave, the old, straggly man puts the boy and the dog down, and the chubby, funny man jumps from his back. The straggly man falls to his hands and knees panting and out of breath. Sitting there the boy starts to cry, "Thank you for saving us, but I am surely dead now. Once the dragon finds me and takes me home, he will destroy everything I have ever loved, and I will have to bear it all. Why, oh why didn't I just stay home instead of running after something when I didn't even know what I was chasing? Why couldn't I have just stayed content instead of asking for the world? I want more, but now I am doomed to lose what I have." The straggly man yells at the boy, "Now, stop your crying! Are you home? Has the dragon taken you home yet, sat you down, and made you watch as he destroys everything you once loved?" Now, as the man yells sternly at the boy, Malachi is taken back by his questions, "NO," he answers! The straggly man continues, "Then, why are you crying about something that hasn't even happened yet? You'll have plenty of time to cry after it happens if you don't hurry up and act now. We can stop this foul beast and save your family, your home, and everything you love, but we can't do that sitting here crying about something that hasn't even happened yet." The boy stands up, and wiping the tears off his face with a determined look in his eyes says, "Let's figure out how we are going to do this." The straggly man says, "I heard there is a dwarf living in the mountain who can build a sword that can withstand any flames. It can be made with the same metal that has already once pierced the armored scales of the great beast. If we can go find this dwarf, we can ask for his assistance of time and expertise to craft this sword for us to take and destroy the foul monster once and for all." The boy is dumbfounded by the old man's bravery and courage, "This dragon won't take everything from me without at least a fight!"

The Dwarf and the Sword

Some of the newly found friends start their walk toward the mountains to find this dwarf and their hope in a sword that will indeed destroy the all-powerful dragon. The boy asks the old man how he knows so much about this dragon. He replies, "This infamous beast rules this land with the flames of hell that spew forth from his stomach. He must be the unmatched destroyer of whatever is in sight of his red, devilish eyes. He has made himself the king of his land and has struck fear into everyone because they know they will not be able to oppose his ruling." The boy says, "That's why you live outside the castle's walls, so you won't give in to the dragon's power." The old man replies in a shameful crackle, "That is not entirely true. No, see my little friend, you are not among brave company when you are with me. I am most certainly the biggest coward I know.

"Long ago, when my village was wonderful, I was a brave warrior: strong, fast, cunning. But, I lacked the best warrior attribute.... bravery. See, one day I was practicing my archery when our village's watchman got news from a spy that the dragon was coming to destroy our kingdom. You see, the dragon is an evil destroyer. What he wants is to annihilate everything in his path. We all knew this, so we thought we better surely run! My father said, 'My brothers, my sons, what should we do?'

"The argument began, 'We should run. No, we should stay and fight!' My father spoke up, 'We do not have the time to argue. I say, if you must run, then run, for this is a battle we are sure to lose, but I will stay and fight because I know if I do not, then I have already lost.' There is a small cheer from some of the men, but the others and I started running, crying out, 'I am sorry, but we must live to fight another day.' My father and the brave warriors fought and died that somber day. The dragon burned our kingdom to ashes, nothing remained but dust and smoke rising from the embers; not even the chirping of a lone dove could be heard in the aftermath. A permanent darkness enveloped the land.

"Yet, as for the cowards and I, we survived; we escaped, but not for long, as the dragon caught up to the cowards and enslaved all of them. But, as for me, I told you I was fast; I made it to a hole in the ground and hid there listening to the screams as I heard my brothers and friends being captured. I am safe, but I am the lowest man on earth as I found out that day that even though I am very fast, sorrow is still faster. It caught me and destroyed me more than the dragon ever could. It torched me far worse than any flames from the devil's lungs could burn. I envied my father and those brave men because they died once for me, and I was slowly dying every day. In their death was righteousness but in mine was a narrow escape just to be tortured to die within myself again and again. Oh, how I envy them and wish I could have been brave with them instead of a lonely coward. See my friend, a short life is not a waste of life, and a long life is not necessarily a good one either. What makes your life is not the time but what you do with it. It is not about the years in the life but rather the life in the years." The boy, was taken aback by his elder friend's words thinks to himself, "If I was in his same predicament, I would hope that I could be brave." Then, abruptly in mid-thought, the funny man expresses himself in his rhythmical way, "Mistakes make us great if we do not lose our heart. It helps us bring together things that can come apart."

Feeling for the first time that his elder was vulnerable, the boy chimes in with an honest but assumed stance, "This doesn't make me think less of you. You are my friend, and saving us took as much courage as I have ever seen any hero personify." The boy's encouraging words and admiration gave the old man a crack of a smile. As he places his rather large, ruff, aged-looking hands on the boy's head, he remarks, "Thank you, your believing in me gives me more reason to believe in myself."

And, walking along the road to the mountains, this newly formed group of misfits finds what most people lack finding their entire lives. They found, through their troubles and honesty, the ability to trust one another and that trusting and care make for the best of friends. As the boy sat back he thought, "I have made something here that I will surely miss if I make it home. Yet, I couldn't have survived without my friends, and as sad as it might be if I get to leave them, I'm still so glad that I found them." Then, overcome with joy, the lovable dog jumps on the boy in a playful manner interrupting his thoughts, reminding him that life is still going on around him. The two begin to laugh an infectious laugh that soon permeates the entire group as they hike their way toward a mystery to get to the mountain and find the dwarf.

The Friends' Bond

The newly formed group of friends walk together through the forest bonding. In a very abrupt yet quaint way they learn a lot about each other. Still, Malachi wonders where his little boat has floated him. So, he asks the dog, "How long have you lived here, and how long have you been outside the city? Why are you outside the city?" The dog really didn't see this as a bad situation as he could always find the happy things in life. The dog is the type of friend anyone would love to have and one the boy needs. The world could be burning down and the dog would say, "Look at the marvelous fire, so big, powerful, and pretty. I am so glad to be alive to see such a magnificent sight."

Now, you might be thinking to yourself how blind and ignorant that animal is, but in a lot of ways the dog is exactly right. Everything can have a good and a bad side to it, and life is so much more precious and blissful if you choose to just look at its beauty.

You can go around being happy in this world if you just choose to find the good in all situations. The contrary is true as well; you can always find a problem with something, always find a reason to feel sad, or a reason why something is bad, and in certain cases it's necessary to look at both sides of the coin; but, more times than not, if you want to make a bad day good, just look at it in a different way, and that is exactly what this dog always does. The dog simply knows what makes him happy and is loyal like any good dog should be. So, he goes with the people that make him happy and stays at the places that make him happy. The dog tells the boy, "My master is Sir Elmer, and when I was young Sir Elmer trained me and fed me. He took me on many adventures and loved me. So, I follow him because he is my friend and my master. So, if he is outside the gate I am outside the gate, and I will help and follow you because you are my friend too, and that's what friends do." The boy leans down and gives the dog a scratch on the head, and the dog returns the affection with a lick to Malachi's face.

Talks to Sir Elmer

After talking to the dog, Malachi figures out that he probably won't ever get a complete answer to why all his newfound friends are outside the stability of the city's giant gate. The boy thinks to himself, "Maybe that funny man can give me an answer. He is definitely complex even though he is not complex in stature." The boy knows that his answer might not be one he can decipher as it will probably be described in a rhyme or riddle that the funny man is prone to talking in, but he decides to ask him anyway. Kindly, the boy says, "Sir, may I ask how is it that you need to be outside of the city's gate?" The funny man turns around with his hands by his sides and his nose pointing toward the sky and says to the boy, "I suppose I will tell you. So, listen; it was the day that the dragon took my kingdom away. He came to plunder my city so grand. He wants my city, so he forces his hand. But, how dare he come here to face a hero as impeccable as I for it is the beast's own fault if he wants to die. But, I did slip and fall, so he got lucky, and that is all. He hit me with his tail and sent me over the wall which caused me to wail." The funny man turns around with his chest still stuck out while the boy stands directly behind him fighting back laughter. This funny man lives in his own world where he is king. Yet, in reality, he attempts to enlist in the city's army, but they turn him away because he is rather fat and funny looking. Instead, he becomes a jousting clown for the pleasure of the king. In his mind's eye, however, he is a great, proud, and essential guard to the king, and he holds himself in that manner. In fact, he so believes he is such a beloved guard that one day in the middle of his comedy show a man came to usurp the king, and Sir Elmer jumps into action jousting with the intruder until the attempted murderer could be seized by the guards. From that day forward, the king appoints him as Sir Elmer instead of the clown named Elmer.

Now, to everyone else this little man did seem funny indeed, but he sees himself as serious and takes himself as such. Through all the laughs he listens to himself and becomes, rather actually believes that he is a respected man, even earning the admiration of a king because of what he sees within himself. It's all in how you see yourself, and that in turn will be how you project yourself to others and the world and eventually will be who you become.

A Flower, An Elk,
and a Prince in the Forest

As the friends are walking along in the forest, the boy begins to look around at the scenery. He sees tall, old, evergreen trees oddly mixed with palms and maples and he thinks, "What a peculiar forest. It has every tree from all over the world in one forest. I wonder what other things I might see." Scanning his eyes through the forest, the boy's attention is caught by an old man wearing a beautiful garment as colorful as a Japanese kimono and standing as still as a statue, just staring at the ground. His curiosity gets the best of him as he looks ahead to the group who so intently seems focused on the path ahead that they don't notice him sneaking off to check out the interesting man. Malachi quickly tiptoes off as his friends continue on their way.

The boy comes to the old, well-dressed man and says, "Sorry to bother you, but what is it that you are looking at?" But, the old man does not reply. In fact, he doesn't move at all, so the boy looks over his shoulder to see the glimmer of a breathtaking flower. The boy says, "That is the most beautiful thing I have ever seen; I must look closer." The boy knelt to see this wonder of a flower up close and drink in its magnificent beauty with his eyes. It seems to have every color and every variation and shade of color in it, and the colors are perfectly distributed among its hundreds of petals. It is so soft and kind, simply asking to be looked at and admired but demanding your eye in the most enticing way. The boy is mesmerized and completely forgets about the world around him, overwhelmed by the seductive nature of the flower.

The boy was still until suddenly he felt a ram against his side that knocks him down and averts his gaze from the flower. Looking up, he sees that over him stands a dark brown giant elk urgently crying to the boy, "Keep your eyes on me! I have seen this happen before." Sensing the elk's seriousness, Malachi keeps his eyes peeled on the powerful elk as he guides him away from the flower to a safe distance behind the statue that used to be a man. Confused by what is happening, the boy asks the elk, "Why did you not want me to look at that flower?" Moving his jaw from side to side, the elk answers strongly while grinding his teeth together, "The look that you gave that flower is the same look that man gave it so many years ago, the same look he's still giving it today."

The Search for True Beauty

S till not sure how to put the story together, Malachi asks the elk, "Who is that man?" The elk replies more calmly, "I don't know exactly, but what I do know is that man seems to be a prince from a far-off land, and he was trying to wed the most beautiful girl in all of existence so that when anyone saw her they would be very jealous. Not only that, but the prince also appreciates beauty, and he can only stand looking at the most aesthetically pleasing things and people in the entire world, so he made his mind up that he would find the most beautiful woman and wed her at once. So, he asks around to all his subjects to find out who is the most beautiful girl in all of existence. But, to his surprise, so many different people have so many different opinions on who is the most beautiful.

"Out of frustration that no one can give the one straight forward answer the prince desires, he calls for one of the kingdom's wise men and the prince asks him who the most beautiful girl in all of existence is. The wise man gives his answer with a question, 'What is beauty? Describe to me what you mean by beauty.' The prince angrily retorts, 'I don't know, when you look at something or someone you just know whether there is beauty. And, I want in my possession whatever is the most beautiful. But, why must I explain this to you, aren't you supposed to be wise?' The wise man replies, 'The most beautiful things might please the eye, but they undoubtedly please the soul more. So, for you, I do not know what the most beautiful thing or person is, but your soul does. I don't know because we all see beauty differently.' Infuriated, the prince screams, 'You're no wise man! You can't even answer my question. Leave now!'

"The prince, more puzzled than ever, goes to his library filled with quaint and unusual books to search for the answer to his burning question. There he finds a book titled, The Most Beautiful Thing in Existence. He reads from the old, brittle pages where it tells that if you see the beauty of this thing it will make you be envious of whoever holds its beauty that it just sits there to be admired. Brothers have killed one another over it as it is the most coveted beauty in all of existence. The prince, feeling like he had finally found his answer, reads on to discover that it is on the island we are on now somewhere in the forest, so the prince set sail directly to this forest in hopes he can see this most beautiful thing. He comes to this island, and as fate would have it, he becomes lost in the forest. He comes to me for answers, 'I am looking for the most beautiful woman in the world to wed; perhaps you have seen her.' Truthfully, I tell the prince, 'I am sorry, but I am blind. I cannot see beauty; I can only feel it.' The prince replies, 'I am sorry for your misfortune, but you must be able to see to recognize beauty. Perhaps you are mistaken about what beauty is,' he countered.

"Offended, but still trying not to be confrontational, I answer, 'Perhaps, I have been blind my whole life, but my other senses are quite extraordinary because of my lack of sight. I can hear your footsteps, locate you by sense of smell, taking in the scent of your perfume to know your great wealth. I feel your presence and know you are here, so perhaps I can never understand the sight of beauty, but maybe you are the one who is without vision, truly confused on what true beauty is.' The prince, knowing my disability, laughs and says, 'I have come all this way. I would at least like to meet her so it is not a completely wasted trip.'

"That is when he saw it. I could feel his whole demeanor change. His attention is stolen the second he laid eyes on this marvelous flower. 'It is so beautiful. Elk, do you smell its aroma?' Stepping away from him, I want to agree that the heavenly fragrance is indeed beautiful, but then I realize that smell doesn't define beauty. 'If you could only see it, just the sight of it explains why I am in this world, what the meaning of life is, and why there is life. Oh, how I wish you could see it. I think I'll watch it for a while.' I reply again, 'No, you must find your queen, someone to help you rule your land. Besides, sight alone doesn't define beauty.'

"The prince angrily retorts, 'Shut up, you imbecile! If you truly know what beauty is, then tell me what it is.' What I believe true beauty is can be discovered when a mother hugs her child or the sound a stream makes as it trickles across mossy rocks, or the sound of birds chirping nearby. The prince shouts, 'Leave me alone!' While gazing into the flower that almost completely captivates him, he addresses me once more, 'That is why you are blind; you cannot see true beauty.' As I walked away, I thought, 'Being blind doesn't always just mean you can't physically see because today I met a true blind man, ashamed of his weakness about his eyes.'"

The boy simply tells the elk, "Thank you. I believe I should find my friends. We have an important task at hand. There is simply no time to be staring at dormant flowers." As the elk runs off into the forest, his reply can be heard trailing in the wind behind him, "I believe you're right."

All at once, the boy knew that flower must be very powerful because of its beauty, but that beauty it holds is for the eyes alone because its attributes are gut-wrenching and hideous. That beauty it holds can make you feel as though life is so clear and wonderful. The beauty alone explains the most marvelous things in life and why we see meaning in all of them. Yet, the same beauty can make you feel immense confusion and pain, bringing to life the reason to die, the morbid understanding of loss, death, and decay. The most beautiful thing you love, the object of your desire, that helps you feel alive and live life to the fullest, can also be what leads to your downfall. You will only see it when the failures of other people's descriptions of beauty have been awakened in your mind. Then, it will be clear that what is ugly can be beautiful, just as what is beautiful can be ugly. Don't find the beauty without also seeing the ugly as it distorts truth and corrupts complete understanding. Yet, the serendipity in that is ugly and beauty don't have to be kept separate because with so many different viewpoints defining each, nobody has to be alone. Everyone can believe what they want, forming their own opinion of what creates truc beauty.

The Fortune Teller

While passing through the forest, the boy runs across a strange tree that has an old, faded, wooden door covered in ivy, and over top of the door are the words fortune teller. The boy, giving into his curiosity, thinks aloud, "What can this gypsy possibly tell me?" Malachi approaches the door of the tree and begins to knock. He hears a crack and a crick as the door begins to slowly open, pouring a cloud of smoke into his face as he coughs. Out of a smoke-filled room he sees the rather eccentrically dressed gypsy. By her attire, she seems to love opulence as she is adorned with brightly colored scarves made of the finest silk and dripping in chains of gold. The gypsy invites him into her dwelling with hesitance. The boy slowly enters, but as soon as his foot hits the ground in her tiny abode the gypsy's demeanor changes and she clarifies, "That will be twelve coins before we begin." The boy thinks to himself, "Conniving, greedy, gypsy," but he proceeds to pay her anyway. The gypsy sits the boy down and out from under the table she pulls out a clear, glimmering, crystal ball and puts the boy's hands on it as she begins to move her hands over his and make all sorts of hums and ums that the boy has never heard before from a fortune teller. The boy stops her and asks, "Are you sure you can tell the future?" The gypsy says, "Of course, of course I can; do not worry young man." Malika pleads, "Please, I beg of you, don't lie to me, gypsy. If it's not in my future, don't tell me." The gypsy, hearing his plea, spares no feelings, "Because you want the truth, I will give it...someday, somehow, and at some time, you will die!" After speaking her words, she quickly takes the crystal ball off the table and opens the door insisting the boy leave.

Feeling cheated, Malachi grabs the crystal ball and puts it back onto the table. Turning to the gypsy, he says, "That is in no way a prediction; anyone can say that; anyone can say I will be in a grave someday. Risking everything I love, I must know what is to become of me?" "Why are you so concerned with what will become of you?" the gypsy calmly asks. The boy says, "Because if I know that I will succeed, then I can rest easy and my mind won't be in such a frantic state." The gypsy replies, "And, if you know you won't succeed, then what?" Stopping to ponder this, he answers, "Then, I can presume I don't know." Taken aback by that thought, the gypsy gives the boy some insight, "I have been a poor gypsy my whole life traveling from land to land. You see, you shouldn't always know what's going to happen next. If I did, I would not have moved. Instead, I would be a doormat, a vessel waiting on my impending death. See, if I tell you that there is a road you must travel and that road will put you through tortures that are unimaginable, yet all the pain could be occasionally and randomly blessed with things that end up making it all worthwhile, but you might miss or not get some of these blessings, would you still travel it?" The boy pauses and says, "I hope I would travel the road if I must, but it would make it much easier to begin my travels if I didn't know all those bad things were coming." The gypsy with her crystal ball looks at the boy with a strange gleam in her eye and mutters through half-clenched teeth, "See, it's not always good to know what happens next."

You cannot worry so much about what will happen or what won't because in the end what will happen will happen; and, if you don't try to deny it and just take a second to look, you can find reason and meaning in all that happens. The boy looks down and thinks, "If I knew what I had then, I would have never gotten so angry and left on that sailboat. But, if I had never gotten on that sailboat, I would have never come to know what I truly have." The gypsy speaks up, "Since you have been to so many lands, do you know how to get to my island?" The gypsy, in ironic fashion, not being able to tell the future, could not remember her past and simply says, "I know of many islands but not of any one specifically. All I know is that all islands are in the ocean, so try there." The boy, walking off into the forest, thinks to himself sarcastically, "Yes, the endless ocean, that is so much help," yet he keeps his cynicism to himself simply saying, "Thank you" before exiting her tree.

The Lion in the Cave

As the group continues with their journey, the day begins to settle into a deep, dark night to the point the friends could barely see each other. The straggly man says in symbolic fashion, "It seems as if someone is covering up the moon for its slumber, so I think we should sleep as well." Then, rain begins to drizzle down, so the boy interjects, "We must find shelter." The dog, off to his own thoughts as usual, joyfully concludes, "I love hearing the rain when I sleep." Still, paying little attention to the dog's remarks, the group searches for a place where they can sleep and be dry from the rain. Just then, out comes a relieved shout from the funny man, "Look over here. There is a cave, don't you see, have no fear?"

Delighted by their good fortune, the group heads toward the cavern for rest. Once inside the cave, they could not see each other in the pitch blackness, so the so-called straggly man yells out to the group, "With the darkness of night comes lower temperatures, so we must make a fire to keep warm and to be able to see." So, the group begins to feel around on the ground for something to use to start a fire. The boy calls out, "I have found what feels like a dry branch with dry leaves." The straggly man reaches out toward the boy's voice and grabs the branch, breaks it in half, and starts to rub them together creating friction that soon lights the leaves that he strategically places at the bottom of the two sticks. The boy sighs in relief and looks up to thank the straggly man when suddenly his words were stolen from his mouth by the sight of giant, green, thin, feline-shaped eyes peering directly over the straggly man's head. The boy begins to shake and stammer terribly as the group jumps around to see what it is that has the boy so spooked. They see what the commotion is about when suddenly the face of a lion comes out of the darkness unexpectedly. This creature, however, doesn't look fierce at all. Instead, the poor lion looks malnourished and weak, and at his feet lies a crown that is broken in half with rare jewels that have been scratched and shattered.

The boy looks at the lion with a heavy heart and says, "Hello." The lion hesitates before responding, "What is hello?" Malachi responds, "It is a greeting to acknowledge one another's existence." The lion continues, "Why do we need to greet one another? Is it to insure we aren't dangerous? Does hello show our intentions? Does hello imply I care about any of you surviving? Hate me if you wish, but if I make your survival more bearable you will love me and never leave, that is until I give you any sign that I may be jeopardizing your survival in some way." The boy is unsure how to answer because the lion speaks well over his head, "I simply meant hello," he stammers. The lion quickly interjects, "You simply mean hello you say, but you do not understand intention or why you speak at all. We are stupid beings that are at the disposal of an infinite galaxy that was here before your conscious self and is sure to be here after your conscious self. We are well designed robots whose brain chemicals can change our every move. But, I wonder why we want to survive. After all, this is the one thing most every living organism shares, the need to survive this existence. I was a king once, just look at my broken crown. I assume the meaning of life is to be loved, but I did all the just and right things so that all my people would love me, but no matter how many ways I have tried to please them there will always be those who disagree. They hate me for the same decisions I make to have the others love me. I have spent all my time and effort on making my people happy so that I can be adored by them, but all my efforts were to be lost when they deemed me as no longer adequate to be a king and all my followers, friends, and family banished me from there pack. So, now I find solitude in this cave. The truth is that you only have the people on your side if you are pleasing them. You can accomplish great feats, but it is all for nothing as soon as it is over, like a castle of sand built up until the waves of time washes it away. My feats are worthless, just as your feats will be worthless. Life is simply without purpose." The boy, a tad offended by the lion's lack of faith in life, asks, "It seems as if there is nothing good. Everything is wrong and terrible, so why do you even bother to wake up in the morning?"

While contemplating the boy's question, the lion roars his reply, "Because boy, I simply do. My body wakes me up, and so I suppose that is my purpose, to wake up and see what happens. I'm here, and being here holds purpose though I'm not sure of what, quite frankly. I assume I am missing something, so I cannot die until I know all the answers. I guess that is my purpose." Compelled by this epiphany, the lion walks off into the night and says to the group,

"Sleep well. I am going to go look for something." You see, at that moment the lion realizes that everyone lies. Your life can be a terrible, hopeless endeavor of senseless pain that can end more tragically than it began, but that is just one season in your ever-changing life. Don't give up during the bad times in your life for things can change to good. You are alive, so you are a survivor. But, sometimes your mind needs to be told what your body already knows, that you're a fighter. No matter what, your body will fight and try to survive until it simply cannot any longer as should you, and your mind realizes that surviving is of great importance. Even if I don't know exactly why right now, I know there is a reason my body chooses survival when my mind does not because just choosing not to give up begets hope. Therefore, your body doesn't give up until its dead, and it doesn't die without a fight. That fight shows the body hope, that possibly things can get better. Even when your mind forgets, your body will not.

The Transient

As the group of friends head on their way continuing their journey, they stumble upon a transient man blocking their path ahead. The eerily brooding man has a draping hood over his face. Out of curiosity the boy approaches the transient man and notices him holding an ever-so-smooth piece of wood. He seems to have carved it into some rather peculiar pictures. On the top left corner is a very descriptive tree. Not only did it depict the trunk, limbs, and leaves; it also shows the underlying roots so vividly drawn, telling the tree's struggles and maneuvers past the rocks that unknowingly seem to block the massive tree from its nutrients. "How elegantly complex the roots are under the tree and what a story they tell," the boy thought. The boy notices that by the tree sits a man and more of a stick figure that is drawn without any fine details. One could be almost certain this man is in deep thought, and the stick figure seems to be gazing in wonder, deeply contemplating his confused existence. Once again, surveying the scene, the boy looks down to the bottom right hand corner where there seems to be a poorly drawn man who you can see right through into his body where there is drawn a realistic heart. Veins stream from it that oddly look like the tree's roots. To the left of the heart are written words in all different cases, some carved big while others are carved small. It says: Why ARE WE Made UPof LITtLe OTHer

ThiNgs? And, as the boy got finished reading the statement on the translucent paper, the man slowly turns the slab of wood over, and on the back it says in the same weird lettering: wHy IS the WoRLd MADE up Of LiTtle Other ThingS? MayBE wE ARE tHe little Things that MAke up oTher LITTLE tHinGs ThaTmAKe up Existence.

After seeing the boy get finished reading the statement, the ragged, broken-down transient asks, "Do you notice what these things have in common?" Too startled to answer, the boy just stands there, and the transient says, "There is more to everything than what you can only see." The nomad pauses and speaks again, "You have a you in you, and I have a me in me." The boy reaches into his pocket and drops the transient some bread before going back to his friends. As they continue their journey, he thinks to himself, "What a mysterious man."

The Tortoise

As the friends finally approach the mountain where the great black-smith resides, they see a very elderly tortoise. Everyone knows tortoises move very slow, but this tortoise moves particularly slow, for every step she takes is like the pace of a huge, slow-moving glacier, not noticing the movement unless the start point is marked. When the day ends, return and observe that a little progress has been made. Still, movement is movement, and no matter how slow this tortoise is, she is still going somewhere. The old, straggly man passing by tips his hat to the tortoise and says while creeping along, "Lovely day Mrs., isn't it?" The funny man and the dog follow along shortly behind, and the funny man says, "Lovely day Madam," and speaking softly to the dog so that the tortoise couldn't hear he says, "She must know Adam and Eve." Then, the tortoise as slowly as she is walking replies ever so slowly, "Yes, what a lovely day to climb a mountain." The boy hears her say climb a mountain, so he stops and asks in disbelief, "So, you are going to climb this whole mountain?" The old tortoise replies, "Yes, as high as I can get." The boy asks, "Why are you climbing this when we could carry you up it instead so you can get where you need to go faster." The old tortoise replies, "No, I want to climb this mountain all by myself, so I can say that I listened to my heart, and I climbed a mountain all by myself. That is why I am climbing today because I woke up two weeks ago and felt the need to climb a mountain, so that is what I intend on doing, climbing this mountain." With concern, the boy says, "But, you can't climb a mountain because you are ummm...." Stopping him in his tracks while replying faster than she had in years, the tortoise says, "I'm old, but old or not I am alive, and being alive gives me the perfect amount of time to do what my heart desires. You are never too old for there is always something to be desired. Keep looking and longing for the desires of your heart and stay young at heart." The boy smiles at the tortoise and she smiles back and says, "Now, move along. We are both moving, so I know we are trying to listen to our heart's desires."

Asking the Dwarf to Make a Sword

Getting closer to their destination, the old, straggly man says, "Just over that way between the two rocks is the dwarf's cave. Stay behind me as he is not always good with strangers." As the group walks into the dwarf's cave, the old man makes their presence known screaming out, "Dwarf! It is I, your old friend, and I have brought my friends along with me." Out of the shadows pops a fully-grown man the height of an infant, but with the stature of a giant. He aggressively responds in a deep and powerful voice, "Who are your friends and why all of you here are?" The straggly warrior says, "We are here to ask you for a favor." The dwarf replies in a sarcastic tone, "Favor, everybody always asks for favors, but what might I possibly help you with?" See, this dwarf has a rude personality at times and has a very hard exterior, but inside he is a very loyal, caring man. This just proves one can't always judge a person by senses alone, doing so could mean missing out on very important people in our lives.

Instead, look at a person's attributes, how they act around those that can't give them something in return, at least not something visible in return as something special is inside of everyone. Try and find that extraordinary quality in each individual person because doing so will help you more easily find why you are special even when you might not feel like you are. Getting to the point, the old man replies, "We are in a predicament. We need you to make a sword with the same metal that once pierced the infamous dragon so we can kill it." The dwarf laughs cynically, "Kill the great drag-on...Ha, I can't help you there!" The boy yells in desperate rage, "Look, you coward, all you have to do is make a sword, and then you can sit here in your safe cave, and we will kill the beast. I have no choice, for if I don't the dragon will kill everything I love, and that is something I just won't sit around and watch happen." The dwarf begins to laugh at the boy as he looks at him with the seriousness of life and death and says to the straggly man, "Old friend, I love the young one's spirit. I will make you the sword, but the metal has only ever pierced the beast. I never even gave it a significant wound, and the boy is much too small to hold the sword." The old man takes heed, "I know, but the sword is as good of a chance as any to kill the beast. I will train with the sword to become adept at using it, but I alone must face the dragon because I am the most capable to use the sword, and I need to gain my honor back from him." The dwarf agrees, but as he walks off to make the sword, the boy humbly remarks, "You don't have to face the dragon. This is my battle." The man replies, "Nonsense! Because you are my friend, your battles are now my battles. What kind of coward would I be to not help you with your fight? My heart would not allow me to desert you in your hour of need. Because we are friends, I am responsible for you for the rest of my days. It is no longer a choice because you have made such an impact on my life, and I am now affected by your joys and your pains. There is no other way." And, realizing what a friend he has found he says, "I am responsible for you as well." With a grateful heart, the straggly man says, "Yes, that is why we will all train to find the best warrior, so if I need help my friends can assist. Though each person training is important, I have been training to be a warrior the longest. I have fought many battles, so I should be the one with the best chance."

Prepping for Battle

Humbled and astounded by the bravery and selflessness of his friend, Malachi agrees to his wish and vows to train harder than ever to protect his friend if needed. Again, out of the darkness comes the dwarf dragging a metallic sword behind him and hands it to the old man, "I wish you luck my brave, noble friend." The group heads off to train for the battle against the powerful dragon of destruction. As the friends make their way down the mountain they find a wooden forest that is clear of trees in the middle, and they begin to train. The old, straggly man picks up the sword first with great ease, "The first thing I can tell about the sword is that its defense is the swords greatest power. You must allow it to protect you, and when the opportune moment is given to you by your opponent, only then do you attack. Do not let the haste to get the battle over or your fear for safety misconstrue your judgement on knowing the appropriate moment to strike. A true warrior will find excitement in battle because that is the only way to make it through the fight. The thrill of not being safe is what keeps them alive because I tell you safety is not always in fact safe. Safety doesn't ensure life at all because when I felt the most alive was when I was actually in the most danger. Yet, don't live by the thrill alone. Be wise; let your head control your heart and use them both to their full potential because when you use them together you will be the most complete version of a warrior that you can be." The old man then shows his skill with the sword, cutting the air with such a powerful yet elegant and swift technique that it astonishes his friends.

Then, he comes to a precise stop and looking at the funny, chubby man, he says, "It's your turn." The funny man with his chin high and his eyes closed in a rather confident way grabs the sword and points it directly forward proclaiming, "En Garde, Touché! En Garde, Touché! I was the town's back fencer back in the day." The old man says, "Wonderful, now give the boy a try." The funny man bows, getting down on one knee and hands the boy the sword. With determination, the boy places both hands on the handle of the sword and lifts it from the funny man's hands and then immediately plummets to the ground. Determined, Malachi tries to lift the sword again, but it won't budge. Out of frustration, he yells out, "I will never be able to help you all in this battle. If it comes down to me, we are doomed." "You think too much," says the old man. Continuing his thoughts, he rattles on, "You need not worry; you must believe, for if you don't fight the battle in yourself first you will never win a battle outside of yourself." Confirming the old man's point, the chubby man says, "You see the battle within is the battle we fight before the war will begin." The old man chimes in again, "You see my friend, if you win that battle you've already done the hardest part." In dismay, Malachi laments, "How can I help fight if I can't even use the sword?" The wise elder says, "You must think of what you can do, not what you can't. You see, you can't always fight fire with fire for it will only burn everything. Sometimes you need water." The boy says, "I'm small, innocent, and helpless. Maybe I can deceive the dragon and talk to him while you and the chubby man jump out from hiding and ambush him." The old man excitedly exclaims, "Great, and I will be swift with my sword. We will destroy the foul beast before he even notices what hit him." The dog, feeling eager, jumps happily about. "What can I do?" he says as he runs to pick up the sword from the blade's point with his jaws. The group yells out, "STOP!!!" Struck by fear, Malachi screams at the dog, "What are you doing; are you trying to kill yourself? That is the sharpest blade in all the land. I think you should just sit this battle out." The dog begins to whimper from the boy's reprimand until the old man says, "Certainly not, we need him." "But, the boy replies, the dog is not smart. He could ruin this." The funny man speaks up, "If you judge him on how he thinks, you will see him as dumb, but I see him as smart because he is having the most fun." The boy apologizes to the dog and tells the others, "The dog has tons of energy. He can run circles around the dragon distracting him while we execute our plan. The dog's barks will be a deterrent." The old man proclaims, "That is a great plan. It will take us all to take down the beast." The group walks down the mountain with a new appreciation for one another, with a strengthened bond, and a value for each and every member as they head to the city gate to face the dragon.

The Hawk

As they were approaching the gate, a quite large hawk appears to them. This hawk is large but not too much larger than most. In fact, to most, including itself, this hawk is quite normal. He didn't fully land from his flight before approaching the group at a distance to imply that he is going to say something, so the old, straggly man calls out, "Hello!" The hawk squawks rather timidly, "Ummm, yes, hello. I want you to know you mustn't go any farther. It might not be in your best interest." The straggly man replies, "And, why is that?" not fully understanding what he might be implying. The hawk continues with his warning, "There is a very powerful dragon behind that gate, and he destroys whatever he pleases. So, the cautionary thing to do would be to turn around and stay safe." The old, straggly man replies with confidence, "We are very aware of what is beyond that gate, and that dragon is why we came here. We came to destroy the beast, but you have given us a warning because of your concern for our safety. For that, we are grateful. You are a very kind-hearted hawk." The hawk humbly replies, "You are welcome sir, but I am not kind-hearted. In fact, I am rather terrible." The old, straggly man is very confused, "Why do you say that?" The hawk slowly flies down to land and speaks in a very ashamed manner, "...because of what I have done."

Dropping his head and staring at the ground he continues to explain, "Before, I warned people what was beyond that gate, and I also warned the dragon of who was coming for him. I have seen many hopeful opponents of the dragon coming to destroy him, yet I warned the dragon so he could destroy them instead, not because I believe the dragon is a good ruler; it is because I love the dragon's gold, and I love it so much that one terrible day I got wind of an attack that was going to be placed on the dreadful dragon by my brother and his brave friends, and I told the dragon that they were coming for his gold.

"So, aware of the attack, the terrible beast set flame to my brother and his friends and then came to me laughing as he paid me the gold. I never saw myself so clearly as when the gold touched my greedy beak. I then saw my true self, and it was the most disturbing realization. I felt beyond low, and no gold could make me feel better. So, I vowed from that day on I would spend the rest of my measly life warning people of the same place I once lured them into, and that is why I'm a terrible hawk." The straggly man speaks to the hawk, "Yes, my friend, that was indeed a terrible thing to do. You gave up your brother for gold, but your story doesn't depict you as terrible as much as it describes a terrible thing you have done. What makes you terrible is if you continue to do terrible things. But, if you change your past ways, then you will be a great hawk indeed."

With a heavy heart the hawk replies, "I can only try now to do the right thing to make up for the wrong I have done." The old, straggly man says, "Sir, that is all any of us can do, and that is all that I believe is required." As the hawk flies off, the boy thinks of how someone kind enough to warn them of the trouble ahead can go the rest of his entire existence thinking of how terrible he is when in fact his terrible act made him into a kind hawk. The boy simply thinks, "We cannot worry about the things we have done since we cannot change them. We can only change how we act moving forward. We shouldn't worry about what we have been or what we want to be because it will change every day we make decisions, and those decisions will in turn make you who you are."

What Lies Beyond the Gate

As the group of misfit friends close in on their destination, they see the city gate and the fear starts to sink into Malachi as he gazes upon the gate's power. It seems to be a lot bigger than he remembers when he first saw it. The dark, black color of the gate is only a minor reflection of the darkness that seems to hover over the city's walls, maybe there is a far greater evil inside. The day is early, yet the mountain's walls cover the sun blocking it as if the walls were created to keep the city in a permanent darkness. They arrive to the entrance, and the gate begins to slowly open as if the dragon himself is expecting them. The old man, clinching the sword that is tucked away under his worn, ripped rags that he uses as a cloak, says to them, "This is it. We will fight this war that we did not choose because it has been given to us." Admired with the old man's bravery the boy replies, "Spoken like a true warrior." For the first time, Malachi feels like a brave soldier. He is no longer running from his fears. He is walking right into the teeth of them. They walk through the gate that is now cracked open just far enough so they can go through one at a time. Upon entering the city, the group sees many barely alive, almost skeletons as well as those already dead skeletons laying on the dirt-covered ground. They hear the begging of neglected souls starving for food and water.

Now, I have heard of people starving back on my island, but it is something entirely different to see this bleak reality, to feel their presence, to listen to their pleas for help. Hearing them expressing their needs instead of their wants is heart-breaking. They are simply surviving; their agony can be felt. The stench is overwhelming as hygiene is not as needed as food, not as important as their pleas and prayers for basic needs, not desires. I remember when I was younger my mother told me not to waste my food because someone is dying in need of the same food that I put to waste. I didn't understand the importance and am convinced that she didn't even fully understand how true her words were, but to see the story that is told by their visible ribs, their quiet yet loud screams make me ashamed for my abundance.

To think I have coveted my friends' possessions, their giant homes, makes me sick. To think that there are giant homes at all that only house a few is a shocking thought. After all, is a house not for shelter? I see now as I throw away food out of dislike or over- abundance and call it trash, when I can clearly open my eyes and see people literally dying for that trash, literally dying for shelter and comfort, that I truly can't fathom my good fortune against their struggles. I am embarrassed by the greed and gluttony of the rich and the audacity to want or ask for more. Shall we not help these people with mothers too, families, and children? They have ideas, hopes, and fears. They freeze, hunger, and hurt. They have desires too. Where is your goodness if someone has needs around you yet you do nothing but take for your own selfish riches? I ask you, "Have you seen evil?" I do not necessarily think that people of great fortune are truly in full blame for if you have abundance it is difficult not to live abundantly, but our rulers are to blame as well. They tax the wealthy and horde the money for themselves as it is in their best interest to build huge coliseums, cathedrals, or supply weapons to soldiers to fight wars that the soldier has no clue why they are fighting. I don't say there is not a need for that at some point in time, but the needs of the body must be first. You cannot fight a war when you are hungry because war no longer is the priority. Food and clean water are what your body demands. You cannot build buildings when you haven't had water to drink in days. Why don't we meet the most basic needs, making it top priority, and then utilize resources to meet remaining needs? Do not let some go hungry and become weak if you are truly powerful. Now, I know these are just thoughts as it would be impossible to feed the world for I don't have enough resources. After seeing this, all I can hope is that I would never be in abundance when I am in the presence of someone in need.

The old man says, "Let's move along." Despite all the horrors that are going on around them, they look through the dust riddled fog to see a beautiful castle amidst the living hell. It glowed through the darkness with great, white, alabaster walls trimmed with gold and emeralds. The whole roof was made of a red diamond carved to perfection. It appears all the rare minerals and great riches of the earth have been wasted on a worthless shelter to keep the rain off the dragon's head. Yet, the hatred of the dragon isn't enough to hide your eyes from the lustful beauty that illuminates such a hellish, imperfect city.

The castle seems like a heaven-sent deity that came down to the imperfect world to just watch as everything burns all around it demanding the wonder and praise of all the decrepit, dying creatures in its realm. They walk forward until the funny man stops at some moss-covered, crumbled stones. Falling to one knee he softly speaks, "Things have surely changed. Here lies my kingdom, broken and defamed." The boy looks up to see remnants of a broken-down castle with stairs leading high to nothing except the remains of what used to be rooms of kings and queens.

The funny man, shuffling through the boulders of his old kingdom that he held so dearly, finds his beloved king's sword in the rubble. He proclaims, "I will take the dragon's head with the sword of my people who are now dead and gone." The dog, sitting there looking up unto the sky barks, "The dragon is coming!" They all run off in a scramble to get to their places like they had planned. The dog runs off behind the old kingdom's remains and hides in the shrubs behind a wall. The boy stands upon a platform that is left behind after the castle's collapse. The funny man and the old man take cover behind the rubble that is stacked on each side of the boy so they can quickly ambush the beast and slay him before he breathes his deadly flames.

The Dragon and the Battle

The dragon calls out, "My boy, my boy, are you here? I feel you are oh, so close." Malachi, trembling in fear, can't keep his legs from shaking, knees rattling. The dragon articulates each breathy word, dragging them out for his pleasure, "Oh, there you are. You look ready to go home. You seem so very tired. Are you ready?" The boy, stricken with fear, can't even reply. He is like a stone, stiff and unable to move. Malachi looks briefly down to the old man who gives him a wink to assure him of what he is doing. The boy speaks to the dragon, "Please, I beg of you, this one time show me mercy. I will leave here immediately. I will never come back; I will find my home and stay there. Just this once, show me mercy and don't destroy my home and everything that I love. Let me go in peace, I beg of you!" The dragon laughs, "Now, that wouldn't be fair to all the people whose homes I destroyed before yours and the ones I'll destroy after. That is rather selfish, isn't it?" In a loud, demonic roar the dragon yells, "YOU ARE GOING HOME!"

Then, just in the nick of time, before the dragon could grab him, the dog barks. The dragon jerks around breathing fire out of his mouth that just narrowly misses the dog. The old man and the funny man jump from their hiding spots, and the funny man jumps up and strikes the dragon with the sword, but it shatters like glass against his scaly armor. But, it gives the old man just enough of a distraction to strike the dragon with the sword of piercing metal. The old man strikes the beast, and the sword penetrates the dragon's hide. The dragon roars in pain as his blood seeps through his scales. The sword works but is now stuck in the dragon's hide.

Infuriated, the dragon lifts himself up trying to fly away as the old, straggly man leaps up and lunges for the sword but is knocked out of the sky by the dragon's tail. It hits the old man like a battering ram destroying the walls of the fortress, violently plunging him into the crumbling stone wall. The crackle of every bone in the old man's body and the worthless, yet hard gasp for air will ring over all creation for the rest of time. The old warrior, with everything he has left in him, says, "I was sure to lose. I knew I would die, but if I didn't fight then I never lived." The old man, closing his eyes and laying his head back, takes his last breath.

Still frozen, not in fear but in sadness, Malachi can do nothing but fall to his knees. The funny man is no longer funny. He no longer rhymes. He just regretfully cries as he crawls backwards, "I am so sorry. I am oh, so sorry." With a whimper, the dog howls in the most regretful cry. Angered, the dragon yells to the guards, "Seize them!!! Take that old, fat man and that nuisance of a dog to my castle. They shall be my personal slaves. As for the boy, take him to the prison. He will wait for me until I feel like taking him home, and when I do, I will destroy everything he has ever had the slightest fondness of."

Epilogue

I can tell you right now that the story is over. The sad thing, my friends, is that for most people it would be finished. See, I am the little boy, and you are the little boy. Just like our problems and daily struggles in our lives, the dragon seems awfully big right now, and I would be lying to you if I said that everything will end happily for most of us, because our problems can destroy us and the things we don't want will often die just like the people we don't want to die often do, and the people we don't want to live seem to live forever.

But, if you are the boy, what will you do to destroy your problems? Please, I encourage you to write your own ending. Take it from no one else for I, the author, am nobody special, just someone who wrote a story because I couldn't stand the endings of so many others. Most stories are filled with unrealistic optimism. Their happy endings didn't tell me the truth at all; they gave me mistrust that right always prevails. But, that's not always true. Everyone strives for that happy ending letting you know after the story has ended that the heroine has won and thus shall be happy. But, if the story does not end so idealistically, then I should be sad and regard the story as an awful one. I plead with you, do not think that way.

Instead, believe you have what you need and want, and see your story as essential for life. Enjoy living in the present, see your blessings as they come because tomorrow you will miss what you have today. For example, look at the boy, he just wants to go home, but he keeps looking ahead not seeing what a great friend he has in the old man. If the boy ever makes it to where he is going, he will still miss the old man. So, don't be so focused on the ending that you miss why you were meant to read the story. Life is meant to be lived and enjoyed while you are living it. Your life is not meant to be consumed by the thought of when it will be over. You are not supposed to know everything ahead of time for there would be nothing else to learn.

So, live without fear and be happy because whether you win or lose no one can take away the joy you can find today. What I am discovering is it's best for you to create your own ending. Listen to yourself in the present for your world is this world, and you have just as much say in it as anyone else, SO SAY SOMETHING, say exactly what you mean and mean what you say. I tell you that I wrote this story down because the words inside of me beg to be heard. If I didn't listen to my inner self, the same words would enslave my tongue and threaten my very existence. We must not be vain enough to listen to whispers. They might not be loud or put on a show, but they have meaning all the same. Only a true magician can take something of no value to him and make it into one of the world's most valuable treasures. It's not what you do for yourself that makes you good, righteous, holy, or whatever term you want to use. The more you give of yourself, the more you gain. I don't know why it's an anomaly that the more energy we spend, then the more energy others spend on us. Hoarding your riches will not make you rich; it's about being selfless. When you give of yourself, you will find treasures that riches can't buy. So, make your own ending great. Show everyone what makes you happy and what you love so they can love you for it and in turn help others to find and show what they love so they can be loved the same. That is why I wrote this story even after the apprehension of keeping it to myself. I encourage you to share what you love as you write great endings to this story.

After the Battle

S ince no story is going to be read without an ending, I will give you my version of how this boy's story ends. Malachi, laying on the ground, as dooming reality impedes his mind, is stunned by his disbelief and sorrow as to what just transpired. The boy's hands and knees buckled to the ground and every cell in his body is frozen into the form of a statue. His eyes are locked in a gaze as he stares at his lifeless friend the dragon just killed. His hope dies along with his dear angelic friend. The boy can't move as guards march in and seize him. He goes without a fight. Even though he is not scratched from the battle, his will has been beaten to the point he can't move, so the guards drag him to the prison and lock the gate. Malachi is made to wait there until the dragon of destruction decides to come and take him home. The boy sits down pondering his demise, overcome with sadness from the loss of his dear friend. The memory and reminders keep haunting the boy, literally draining the life from him. The boy thinks to himself, "What a great man my friend was. He made me so much better, but he also made it impossible to live without him. I almost wish I never met him." As these thoughts became words, creeping their way out of his mouth much like the saline that began to trickle from his eyes, he mutters, "I miss you."

Overheard by one of the other prisoners the boy got a reply, "....
quite possibly the saddest statement in the world." The boy is beyond
broken-hearted, "It is nothing close to what I feel." The prisoner
agrees, "No, you'll never forget him or stop missing him." After hearing this from the prisoner, the boy feels a jolt of anxiety course
through his body, but it soon subsides as he replies, "I wouldn't want
to; I will never find another friend like him. I don't wish to forget him
at all, but I do wish I had never met him as the pain is just too much
to bear." The prisoner sympathizes, "He'll always be in your memories. You know he'll always teach you something. When someone
teaches you something they are still very much alive." The boy asks,
"What can he teach me without saying anything? I can no longer hear
him." With great belief in his words, the prisoner exclaims, "The most
important things are memories. They aren't just there to make you
sad or make you wish to go back to the past. Memories are meant to
make you remember the good things, so the next time you see something worthy you will cherish it and care for it."

The prisoner continues, "You will always miss your friend, but
the next time you meet someone respectable you will know they will
be a good friend because he was so decent to you. You will love and
cherish the next friendship twice as much because of what your friend
taught you; he taught you the example of what true friendship means.
So, don't be afraid to love because loving and losing only teaches you
how to love more passionately the next time around. When you love
more passionately, they will love more passionately in return. The
only way you ever truly miss out on loving is guarding your heart
against ever loving again or never loving at all." The boy thought of
his old friend and fell asleep with a smile on his face only to be awakened by his impending doom. Opening his eyes, he sees the dragon
of destruction right in front of him laughing through snarled fangs,
"Now is the time you have been waiting for. I am here to take you
home." The guards drag the boy out of the cell and onto the dragon's
scaly back. The dragon takes off into the sky heading straight for the

boy's island. As the dragon is flying the boy back home, he thinks he is surely doomed. Malachi has many regrets as he reflects on how he got to where he is now, "I am lost for sure. Oh, if there is a hero in heaven that can deal with this beast and stop his unremorseful, self-glorified acts of destruction, take from him his reign, and defeat this devil instead of letting him glutton in this victory, devouring hope with his unjustified destruction, then please let him appear and conquer this serpent. I fought so hard to make a path to victory, a path getting crushed by an ever-damning hell that life is filled with terrible lies.

"Now, I know I might seem like I am being a whiny, inconsiderate, ignorant boy that just does the wrong thing at every turn, but I tell you I am just trying to do what is right. I started out with a lot, and it is my fault my heart wanted more. It may be my biggest mistake, but I will never stop following my heart because I want to be happy. I don't want to believe a heartless lie that was fed to me down from the hands of people who were also dead inside. Riches and gold don't pay for good health, and material objects can't purchase pride, hope, and the joys of adventure. No, we must find strength in defeating what makes us weak. I have seen evil, and it doesn't have a disturbing face. It doesn't do much, but what it does do is hinder progression because that is what keeps us alive. Tell me what makes you happy so I can learn and feel your same happiness, and I will love you forever. We must go into action and not just put on an act. Let us survive, thrive, and love to be alive." Thoughts of his friend give Malachi a bolt of courage. Regretting how he wishes he were dead rather than watch everything he loves die, the boy balls both of his fists up, and lifting them over his head, he musters every ounce of strength and lets down all his anger, rage, and power onto the beast's head, but it merely tickles the dragon. A roaring, sinister laugh echoes from the dragon's belly as the boy examines his hands which felt as though they had been crushed by boulders.

"You are going home, my boy, and there is nothing you can do about it. You are hopeless; you will watch as I burn everything you love into nothing but a horrifying memory." The boy, gasping for air, and feeling like there is nothing he can do, no hope he can find of saving everything he once adored, plunges himself from the beast into the ocean below. The dragon quickly notices as the boy splashes into the water, "No, you can't escape me! You are going home."

Cutting through the air like a knife the dragon dives for the boy, but as he hits the water he is overwhelmed by it and his wings flap to a halt as the dragon's body is frozen by the water's magnificence. The dragon opens his mouth to yell, but where fire once flamed is now overrun by rushing water. The water sits on the beast's stomach with the weight of a mountain, and as the boy floats to the surface, the dragon sinks to the depths of the ocean to be forever lost at sea. The boy never felt more at peace as he grabs onto a branch in the middle of the ocean to rest and float for a while.

Awaking the next morning, the boy is astonished and confused. He didn't know if he had been dreaming or if he had died because of the magnitude of beauty in front of him. He is finally home, the warm sun soothing his face as he pushes off his floating log of a raft and swims for the shore. Taking it all in, he finds a new appreciation for the sand that is warm and lodged between his toes. His heart has been longing for this, and now that it is a reality, no dream can suffice what he is feeling. He breathes it all in as he takes off running home screaming, "Mother, Mother!"

Dashing through the breeze blowing in off the shore that cools the island and complements the sun's heat perfectly, the boy sees his home and to him it has never looked so beautiful. The home stood in the boy's eyes with a new sense of pride. Because of his journey, he has a new appreciation for the house and how it came from a tree, broken down into pieces of wood. How dead that tree must have felt all spread apart into hundreds of different pieces and how the tree must have lost all hope just longing to be put back together again. When it felt the most doomed and had completely given up all hope of ever being something or even just put back together as a tree again, a man comes along and picks up all the broken pieces and makes them into a beautiful home for a loving family. It is beautiful, and because the family loves the house, the house returns the family's love and stands tall against the rains, storms, and daily destructions that life will throw at it. Thus, the once tree finds its purpose in being a house and loves itself as a home, finding its pride even though it is broken apart and scattered logs. Even without knowing those logs' infinite potential, the boy now knows what it takes to be something of value, and that it takes losses to fully appreciate things you gain, that life is not just wished upon; it is made alive by living it and somehow once your heart aligns with righteousness, the world will help find a way to heal your heart.

The boy, dashing back into his home, falls into the familiar embrace of his mother. To him, that embrace is so much more special and meaningful now.

He thinks to himself as he grips her tighter, "I wish to never forget her." He will cherish that embrace now and for eternity, knowing what it is like to be deeply loved. If he is honest with himself, he will never get confused by shallow love; he will know and feel the difference. His mother asks in a delighted yet concerned tone, "Son, did you find what you were looking for; did you find who you are?" The boy pauses and says, "I found I am a coward sometimes, but when I need to do what is right I am braver than I ever imagined. I found a true friend and what it is like to be a true friend. I found I am not afraid to die because the fear of death can cripple you from living. I found strength when I was weak, courage when I was afraid, and hope when I was lost. I found I can change, and I most certainly will. I found that I may not be able to do a lot, but I can do something great, maybe not for anyone else but myself, and that is more than I set out to find. I was looking for the world, but I found something better; I found the true me inside myself, the me in me so to speak." The mother smiles in delight and says, "You are a very luck boy; you found riches not everyone has." The boy walks out the door to the ocean that once mocked him for what he lacked. He looks down to his reflection and proudly exclaims, "I know exactly what I want to be, and that is me!"

Now, I told you there was something that I didn't want you to forget, that this boy had forgotten, that is that you are wonderful pieces of this world and that no one else can be you for you are important to this life. I am sure now, after all the boy finds out about himself, that is a reality he will never forget. But, have you found that out for yourself yet? If you make it to the end of this story, I'm sure you will. If not, that is your obligation to find out how important, how brave, and how wonderful you are. The easiest way to accomplish this is to find out just how irreplaceable and wonderful everyone is. Find what you are doing to make this world better and help others find their importance. It doesn't have to be a great big idea that nobody has thought of before, but it can't be just anything either. It must be what your heart desires, and if you listen for it, your heart will tell you what to do. That is how you can find the real you in you, because that is how I found the real me in me.